The poems in this book follow the pattern of the game of *The Minister's Cat*. There is a word for each cat and a poem to go with it; and each cat is followed by a mouse.

The "Minister's Cat" game.

This is an alphabet-game for a group of anything up to about twenty players. You sit in a circle, and each person, on her or his turn, says *The minister's cat is a . . . cat*, filling in the gap with a word to describe the cat. You begin with "A" and work through the alphabet. Anyone unable to think of a word beginning with the correct letter loses a life. On the loss of three lives a player is "out". When you reach "Z" you can go back to "A". You can keep going, if you have the patience, until only one person is left in the game! On the second, third and subsequent rounds you lose a life if you say a word that has alrealy been used by another player.

Poetry by the same author

STANDING ON A STRAWBERRY

First published in 1989 by
André Deutsch Limited
105–106 Great Russell Street, London WC1B 3LJ

Text copyright © 1989 by John Cunliffe
Illustrations copyright © 1989 by David Parkins

ISBN 0 233 98367 8

Printed and bound in Great Britain by
WBC Ltd, Bristol and Maesteg

The Minister's Cat

JOHN CUNLIFFE

A Cat-and-Mouse chase through the Alphabet

Illustrated by David Parkins

ANDRE DEUTSCH

Albert

Anxious Albert,
The Minister's cat,
Will never sit upon the mat,
For fear of mice and things that creep,
Or dreams that come to trouble his sleep.
In a Harrods' bed with a tartan rug,
An electric-blanket to keep him snug,
He curls up tight with his toes tucked in,
But he'll surely wake if you drop a pin.
So, HUSH! — go soft in the Minister's house,
And please don't squeak,
My good little mouse!

Arthur

Artful Arthur,
The articulate mouse,
To see him, you'd think he owned the house.
At arrogant ease in Albert's bed,
He nibbles Albert's honey and bread.
He uses the mat as a trampoline,
And lives on jelly and pink ice-cream.

When Albert goes, at last, to sleep,
Here comes Arthur,
See him creep!
With a whisker-tweak
And a nip on the tail,
He makes poor Albert caterwail!
And just when Albert's nice and snug,
He creeps along and pulls out the plug.
On chilly nights, poor Albert freezes,
While Arthur nibbles the choicest cheeses.

The Minister's cat is a bulbous cat.

Bertie

Bulbous Bertie,
The Minister's mog,
Is game to chase
Any size of dog;
Bulldog, boxer,
or Belgian Hound;
He'll chase them up,
Or out,
Or around.

Brian

Bare-bones Brian,
As thin as a thistle;
The only mouse in the world
Who can whistle;
Entices dogs
Both thin and fat,
To suffer the claws
Of the Minister's cat.

The Minister's cat is a careful cat.

Catherine

Careful Catherine,
The Minister's mouser,
Is an absolutely
Super pouncer;
Mice and rats,
(and other beasts,)
Are the fodder
for her feasts.

Carrie

Carefree Carrie,
The mouse in the attic,
Is casual and careless,
And, oh, so erratic;
When it comes to avoiding
Miss Catherine's claws,
She breaks every one
Of the mouse-world's laws
For surviving the snap
Of a pussy-cat's jaws!
Oh, dear little Carrie,
You mouse in the attic,
I fear that one day
I will find you quite static.
Your plan of escape
Should be truly schematic;
Your luck holds for now,
But it's not automatic!

The Minister's cat is a dropsical cat.

Douglas

Dropsical Douglas,
The Minister's feline,
Will, for any food,
Make a bee-line.
Sausages, cakes,
Puddings and pies;
He gobbles them up
With greedy eyes,
And when he gets
A tummy pain,
He sicks it up,
And starts again!

Desmond

Doleful Desmond,
The dustbin mouse;
Hear him grumble,
Hear him grouse!
Can't eat this;
And won't eat that;
Won't touch sugar,
Salt, or fat.
A mouldy piece
Of rotten cheese,
Will do no more
Than make him sneeze.
He's only got his figure in mind,
When he pushes aside his bacon-rind.

As he goes around
the bins for a jog,
He sees that Douglas
Making a hog
Of himself
With two meat pies;
Stuffing his face
Right up to the eyes.
And he can't touch a thing
For the rest of the day;
I fear, poor thing,
He will fade away.

Eric

Eager Eric
The Parson's Persian,
Loves a story,
In any version.

Edward

Educated Edward,
The mouse erudite,
Lives behind a bookcase;
(The second on the right.)
When he finds a book
Upon the library table,
Edward emerges
As soon as he is able,
To read an earnest elegy,
Or endless epitaphs,
Or have a go at Euclid,
(He's not in it for the laughs!)

But if he finds a story,
In prose or dancing verse,
He turns away in sadness,
With a soft scholastic curse;
His mind's attuned to questions,
Such as, "Why did God make cats?"
Or, "Is there life beyond the trap?"
"Are mice just wingless bats?"

If Eric gets him in his paws,
The ending's never gory,
He simply makes him stay mouse-still,
And listen to a story!

Felicity

Fastidious Felicity,
The Bishop's Siamese,
Loves best quality
Camembert cheese;
She drinks the cream
From the Guernsey milk,
And she sleeps in a basket
Lined with silk.

Only the best of the best
will suffice,
For one who would never
Condescend to *mice*.
She honours the earth
With the touch of her paws,
And lives by none
but Felicity's laws.

The Minister's mouse is a fast-food mouse.

Freddie

Fast-food Freddie,
The mouse at the takeaway,
Of all the mouse-tribe,
He's something of a breakaway;
Pizza-topping,
And quick kebabs,
He'll gobble anything
Up for grabs.
He'll drink from puddles,
Or slopped beer-mugs;
And sleep in a cellar
That's creeping with bugs;
He lives by the
Back-street jungle's laws,
Wary of all
That moves on paws.

Gertie

Grumbling Gertie,
The parson's puss,
Is all of a pother,
And all of a fuss:
Her dinner's too hot,
Her tea's too cold,
And she'll *never*, ever,
Do as she's told.
Tell her to come,
And she's sure to go;

She's contrary,
From top to toe.
Her bed's too smooth,
And the rug's too rough;
The fish too tender,
The meat too tough;
The night's too dark,
And the day's too bright,
And nothing is ever, no *never*
quite right.

The Minister's mouse is a gracious mouse.

Gregory

The Minister's mouse
Is a gracious beast;
Old Gregory comes
To the daily feast
That Gertie leaves
Upon her plate,
And grateful Gregory's
Never late.

Helen

The Minister's cat
Is a hallowed creature,
She really should
Have been a preacher;
Holy Helen
Sits on the stairs,
Just to say
Her morning prayers,
When every person in the house,
Thinks she's watching for a mouse.

She prays each morning,
Noon and night,
And when a mouse
Comes into sight,
"This one," she says,
"Is just my pigeon,
I must convert it
To my religion."
She tries and tries;
If it will not,
She converts it,
To the pot!

For what we are about to receive...

Harold

The Minister's mouse
Is a hasty quadruped,
At the crack of day
He leaps out of bed.
Hectic Harold,
Always in a hurry,
See him scamper,
See him scurry.

Dashing headlong
About his affairs,
He runs into Helen
On the stairs.

Held devoutly
In her paws,
Harold eyes
Her pious jaws.
Gets religion
On the spot,
Just to save him
From the pot.

At times it makes
Good sense to hurry,
To avoid being eaten
In a curry!

Imogen

Imogen, the incorrigible cat,
Sleeps in the Minister's daughter's hat.
She steals the cream and tips the jug,
And lets it pour on the Persian rug;
She dabbles her paws in the milky puddle.
And then, to add to the mess and the muddle,
She makes a pounce on granny's knitting.
Soon about the house she's flitting,
With milky paw-marks everywhere,
Fit to make a Minister swear.

The Minister's mouse is an impresario mouse.

Irving

Irving, the impresario mouse,
Makes his home in the Opera House.
Immaculate in his evening dress,
He views each show with the crowd from the Press.
And, if it's a tale that's just to his taste,
Be sure he'll not have a minute to waste.
He'll gather a cast from his rodent-relations,
For the next in a series of mouse-presentations.
Through a crack in the boards, they'll be learning their parts,
Till each word and note is quite safe in their hearts.
And then, when the theatre is closed for the night,
Oh, what a scamper and gleaming of light!
For it's then the *mouse* theatre will open its doors,
To squeaks of excitement and patter of paws;
They're scrabbling and creeping from attic to cellar,
When "Irving Presents" — "The Mouse-Cinderella,"
"The sound of Mice," or "Porgy and Mouse,"
Whilst "The Mouse of Seville," should bring down the house.
There's even a matinée specially for cats,
They come in a carriage and wear their best hats;
They promise no mice will be eaten that day,
For to do so would surely quite ruin the play:
And Irving's friend, Imogen, sits in a box,
Eating up all of the Minister's chocs!

Juniper

Judicious Juniper is a great joker;
A cat with a face as long as a poker.
He sits looking solemn
In places salubrious,
How ever you greet him,
He'll seem quite lugubrious.
You can stroke him and pet him,
And call him sweet names,
But he'll soon let you know,
He'll have none of such games.
When he rolls on his back
With his legs in the air,
Then that is the time
To approach him with care;
He really does find it
Quite crashingly funny,
If you call him pet names,
Then tickle his tummy.
He'll wait till you're well
In the reach of his paws,
Then trap you and scratch you
With all of his claws.
And then when the Minister
Sees your dismay,
He says, "Not to worry.
It's only his play."

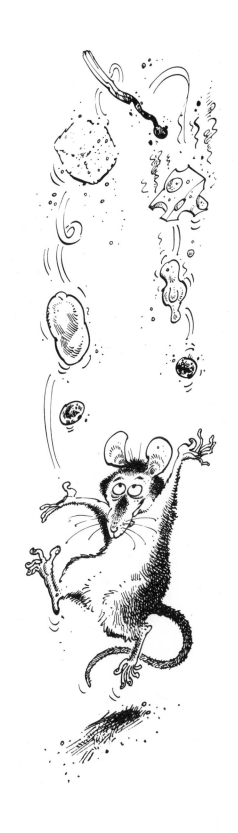

Jules

Jules the juggler;
Household smuggler;
Nuts and bits
Of mouldy cheese;
Peppercorns
To make you sneeze;
Sugar-lumps,
And old match-sticks;
Drips and drops
From candle-wicks;
He sets them twirling
Through the air,
Up and down
The cellar-stair;
Never stopping,
Never dropping,
See the little
Mouse-eyes popping!

Then old Juniper
Comes to see,
Watch the whole
Mouse-circus flee!

And when Sylvia comes
To sweep,
She spots his *juggles*
In a heap;
Says, "How did all this mess
get here?"
Jules whispers,
"I could tell you, dear!"

Katy

Kapok Katy,
Sits sedately,
On the window-ledge
In the afternoon sun.

Kapok filled
from toes to whiskers,
She's not one
Of your kittenish friskers.
She never scratches,
She never fratches,
She never leaps
To open latches.

When the baby
Chews her tail,
You'll never hear her
Caterwail!

And little mice
May safely play,
Where kapok Katy
Holds her sway.

The Minister's mouse is a keep-fit mouse.

Kenneth

Keep-fit Kenneth,
With muscles bulging,
Alas, in kippers,
Loves indulging.
So poor Kenneth's
Getting fatter,
And his paws
No longer patter,
But go THUMP THUMP
About the house like lead,
And wake the Minister
In his bed,
And fill the man
With fearful dread!

Larry

Literary Larry lives in a club,
A place where even a cat can rub
Against the legs of the clever and famous,
And try to discover just what their game is.
(It is said he's been stroked by Kingsley Amis!)
And when they've all dropped off to sleep,
Into the Library our Larry will creep,
And borrow a pen and bit of paper,
To have a try at this writing caper.
But his paws don't quite seem to have the trick,
And soon the paper's not so spick;
And, oh, he hasn't got the knack,
And soon the paper's looking black,
With inky paw-marks everywhere,
And Larry's feeling in despair.
And so he gives up in a trice,
And returns to chasing mice.

Lucretius

Lucretius the legal mouse
Of Lincoln's Inn,
Is grey in the whiskers,
And getting very thin;
For years he's been a'nibbling
At dusty legal tomes,
And, oh, how he longs
For a dish of mutton-bones!

But if some cheese is stolen,
Or if a trap's been sprung,
Or a quarrel's to be settled,
You'll hear his praises sung.

When all the squeaking's finished,
And there's many an aching jaw,
They'll go and ask Lucretius,
The expert on the law!

Malevich

Malevich the macabre cat,
Lives in a haunted tower,
Malevolent and murderous;
Oh, see his two eyes glower.

Marcus

Prince of every cosy
Corner of the house,
Marcus is a truly
Majestic mouse.
He lords it
From the cellars,
To the tiles
Upon the roof,
And all the house-cats
Fear him,
If you're seeking
Any proof.

Nellie

Nellie is
a nondescript cat;
She isn't quite this,
And she isn't quite that.
This week she'll be nocturnal,
Next week she'll sleep all night;
One moment nicely nonchalant,
The next she'll nip and bite.
She's something of a novice,
When it comes to catching mice;
But nefarious and niggardly,
When asked to name her price.

Nigel

Nigel,
The neighbourly mouse,
Is friends with every creature
In the house;
And then next door,
And up and down the street,
You'll hear nimble Nigel's
Pattering little feet.
He's got a "Neighbourhood Watch",
To keep an eye on all the rats;
And he runs a coffee-morning,
For the pigeons and the bats.

He has a wood-louse playgroup,
Underneath a big flat stone,
And he runs a dating-service,
For those who live alone.
So every lonely heart-throb,
All creatures great and small,
Visit Nigel in his office,
Have a chat — and tell him all:
Birds and bees and butterflies,
You'll see them congregate,
Fish, or fur, or feather,
He'll find them all a mate.

Oswald

He was one of the Oswalds,
The famous Oswalds,
From Kirkoswald
You know.
And once,
Long ago,
He wore a bow,
Just to oblige his Mistress,
You know.

The bow caught on a tree,
And a fox came along
Full of glee,
Saying, "I have a hunch,
I've found a free lunch."
He gobbled him in a trice,
And said,
"That was very nice."

Since then,
The Oswalds have been
Less obliging.

The Minister's mouse is an origami mouse.

Osbert

He's an origami mouse,
A piece of folded paper;
He cannot squeak,
He cannot scratch,
He cannot run or caper.

The Minister is a pantomime cat.

Percival

Percival the pantomime cat,
Wears the Minister's
Shoes and hat!
Takes his ease,
with a cup of tea;
Walks about,
like you and me.

He can dance
and he can sing;
He can do
'most anything.
You'll see him
arch his back and purr,
In a zip-up suit,
of nylon-fur.
This is nothing
strange or sinister;
The minister's cat,
is the Minister!

With tail and whiskers
quite sublime,
You'll see him in
the pantomime,
("Dick Whittington"
or "Puss in Boots,")
He'll fill the village
hall with hoots,
And gales of laughter,
Rising to,
the highest rafter.

The Minister's mouse is a pernickety mouse.

Pip

A pernickety mouse,
A clicketty mouse,
A slicketty,
Ricketty,
Picketty mouse.

A quicketty mouse,
A flicketty mouse,
A tapetty,
Snappetty,
Slappety mouse.

That's Pip,
The pernickety mouse.

The Minister's cat is a quaint cat.

Quentin

Quaint as a Queen,
In a flying-machine;
Quentin is seen
On the kitchen-scene,
Washing his face,
With old-fashioned grace,
As he sits
Where he fits
By the fireplace.

He sits so still,
On the window-sill,
Is it stuffed?
Says a muffed
Inquisitor,
(Only a visitor.)

Quentin quivers,
Like Arctic rivers,
With indignation,
At such insinuation;
He's never quick,
But he's certainly wick!

["Wick" is quite in order,
North of the Border.
A "Wick thing" is something alive,
A bug in a rug.
Or a bee in a hive.]

Queenie

Quizzical.
Metaphysical.
She wants to know why.
Who made the sky?
What's in a pie?
Why do bats fly?
Can no one tell her?
Can no one quell her?

Things would go speedier,
If she read the encyclopedia.
She gave it a nibble.
To settle a quibble,
But it tasted quite musty,
Dismal and dusty.
The Britannica,
Began to panic-her,
So she gave up on books,
And searched all the nooks,
Of the Manse.

Now she's learning to dance!

Raymond

Raymond the Ready;
A real old steady.
He's ready
For any
Eventuality;
Errors of man,
Or natural calamity.
There's a hundred tins of cat-food,
Stacked under the stairs;
And then there's equipment,
For running repairs;
Needles and scissors and sticking-plaster,
All will be handy for any disaster.
Candles and matches
In case of a cut;
At the end of the garden,
A small wooden hut;
It's bugged and it's rigged with communications,
And a direct line to the United Nations.

And when you think Raymond
Is having a nap,
He's really just waiting,
For something to snap;
Though all is so quiet,
As calm as can be;
Raymond is ready
To go — as you see.

Ruth

There's a very small chapel
Just under the stairs,
Where the mice of the household
Say their prayers.
And reverent Ruth
Will lead the choir,
And tell a Bible story
In a voice of fire.

Paws together!
In a voice of thunder,
Fills the little
Mice with wonder.
And each and every
Mouse-child knows,
That naughtiness leads
To a pussy-cat's jaws.

The Minister's cat is a soft cat.

Sam

Sam is soft,
And he lives in a loft.
He's ever so nice
To the birds and mice.
He's sweet and good,
And he can't stand blood;
He just *won't* kill,
To get his fill.

When his old mum,
Brought his dinner,
He was getting
Thinner and thinner.
She said *Eat it up*
Or you'll surely die.
But he couldn't face up
To a fat mouse-pie.
She really thought him
A valetudinarian,
Until he decided,
To be a vegetarian.
Now he has beans
And lentil-bake,
And he's slim and fit
And no mistake!

And the mice,
They gather him
Grains of rice,
For Sam is soft
In a way that's nice.

The birds deliver
His fruit by air;
For good old Sam
Has them in his care.

If other cats
Come prowling by;
Sam will pounce,
And make them fly!

The Minister's mouse is a slinky mouse.

Samantha

Slinky Samantha,
Like a panther,
Will slink by the wall
In the dining-hall,
When the Minister
Comes to dine;
She'll sip at his wine,
As he sleeps by the fire;
And then when, at last,
It is time to retire,
She'll wear a silk nightie,
With patterns of gold,
And sleep in a bed
That's incredibly old;
With champagne for breakfast
And cinnamon toast,
Samantha can quite
Justifiably boast,
That it pays to be slinky
In diamonds and pearls,
For much is denied
To the un-slinky girls;
Like parties and dances
And staying up late,
And making the fellows
Queue up for a date.

And when the fat cat
Of the house
Is out hunting;
She'll escape by the trick
Of some judicious shunting
Into the smallest
Of cracks in the skirting.
A very good way
Of disaster averting.

The Minister's cat is a thieving cat.

Tom

Tom, Tom,
The Minister's cat,
Stole some fish
And went like a bat;
Out of the window,
And over the fence;
We've not seen a whisker
Of poor Tom since!

The Minister's mouse is a termagant mouse.

Tabitha

Tabby they call her,
(Sounds more like a cat)
She's just as fierce,
Can you fancy that?
A terrible termagant,
She teaches school,
And you can be sure,
She'll play it cool.

Underwood

Unrelenting Underwood
Is up to no good;
Underwood
Is out for blood.
He's not above
Biting the Minister;
Underwood
Is something sinister.
A monster tom-cat,
Terror of the neighbourhood,
That's Underwood.
Last week,
He killed a young Peke,
And ate it,
In the shrubbery;
The bones
Were rather rubbery.

Watch out for Underwood.
He's up to no good!

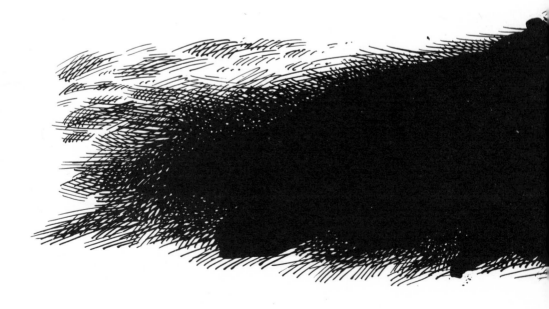

The Minister's mouse is a useful mouse.

Ursula

Useful Ursula,
Gives advice,
To caterpillars, beetles,
Bats, and mice.
And if they need
Some baby-sitting,
Ursula comes
And brings her knitting.
(She only knits up
Useful things,
Like winter muffs
For beetles' wings.)

If you have Ursula
As a guest,
You'll find she's something
Of a pest;
For advice
That's everywhere,
Is something that
You cannot bear.
From apple-pie
To writing a letter,
Ursula knows
A way that's better.
Although you take
No further heed,
She gives advice
You do not need.

Then you must turn,
And sweetly say,
*Ursula, darling,
Go away*!
If she'll not take
Advice that's good
Send her to advise
Old Underwood!

Vanessa

She was there after breakfast,
At her ease in the hall,
A minute later,
She was nowhere at all!
We searched all the house,
Even out in the park.
We found not a whisker,
Not so much as a paw-mark.
There was old Fred,
In his place on the wall,
But our Vanessa
Was nowhere at all.

We went to the shop,
And we bought her some fish,
And arranged it so nicely,
In Vanessa's own dish.
The smell will attract her,
She'll be here in a trice.
Such tricks with Vanessa,
Alas, cut no ice.

The fish lay and wilted,
For half of the day,
Then Fred jumped down
And stole it away.

We asked all the neighbours,
We rang the police;
We knew, till we found her,
We'd never have peace.
Had she been cat-napped?
Or squashed by a bus?
You never did see
Such a pother and fuss.

A week went by
And no sign of the creature,
And the local paper
Made it a feature.
She left such a gap
In the shape of the day;
Nothing seemed right,
Since she vanished away.

After a month
We said *Well – that's just that,*
We've sure seen the last
Of our favourite cat.

We bought a sweet kitten,
Vanessa-the Second;
She was good and obedient,
And came when you beckoned.
And then, when our sadness
Was almost reversed;
In through the door walked
Vanessa-the First!

Where have you *been to?*
We said in surprise,
But she looked all about her,
With innocent eyes.
You'd think she'd walked out
Just a moment before,
As she rattled her dish
With the tip of her paw.

Now we have *two* cats,
Who soon became friends;
And this is the way
That a good cat-tail ends.

Vervain

Vervain is a velvet mouse,
The quietest creature in the house;
With beads for eyes,
And green felt ears,
She lived in the sewing-box
For twenty years.
But now she's gone
And none can tell,
Where in the world
She's come to dwell;
Only a little kitten knows,
Who came and pounced
On silent paws,
And carried her off
To some secret spot,
There in the earth
To lie and rot.

William

William has odd-coloured eyes,
One blue and one black,
And he sits looking wise.
And you sit looking back.

He'll make no sound,
And you'll think him profound;
You'll not realise,
His entire surmise,
Is concerned with mice,
But you'll know in a trice,
If dinner is in course of preparation,
That food is the subject of his cogitation.

But William *looks* wise,
With his odd-coloured eyes.

The Minister's mouse is a whispering mouse.

Wendy

The house is full of whispers.
Is it the Minister at his vespers?
Or Wendy passing messages,
Along the echoing passages?

Ximenes

He came to us
On Christmas Day.
He walked across
The snowy garden,
And came in with the milk.
He adopted the house
And everyone in it
From that moment;
Took us all in his care.

A modest cat.
A quiet cat.
His eyes spoke -
I will be no trouble to you.
I will keep evil from your door.

And we had good fortune
From that day.

Xenophon

It's a very small xylophone,
Made from pegs dropped in the garden;
But, if you're all alone
In the house,
With the radio off,
And the television off,
And you listen to the silence,
For a long time,
You may hear its faint music;
Xenophon on the sticks.
Ghost music, that pricks
Your ears
Like a remembered secret.

Yeats

Old Yeats
He is a Yogi-cat,
A mystic from the East;
He sits quite still for hours and hours;
A meditative beast.
You may just think he's sleeping,
A-dreaming out his days,
But if you dare to say so,
He'll fix you in his gaze.
His yellow eyes flick open,
And look you through and through,
And then you turn embarrassed,
And know not what to do.
Just address him quite politely,
O! Philosophic cat!
And speak of things eternal,
Of *Life* and things like that.
You may speak of many matters
Of a transcendental kind;
You may praise his paws and whiskers,
But pay tribute to his Mind,
And he will look upon you
With calm benevolence,
Even though your words to him
Make very little sense.

The Minister's mouse is a Yorkshire mouse.

Yasmin

Yasmin is a Yorkshire mouse;
She says *Hey up*! and *Get agate*!
And never leaves a single crumb,
Upon her breakfast-plate.

Ex Yorkshire Pud.!

Zebedee

A zany zig-zag cat,
He runs this way,
Then jumps that.
In and out
About the house,
Seeking for
A zig-zag mouse.
He'll never catch one,
Silly fig,
Because the mice
All go zag-zig.

Zeno

This mouse is so zealous,
It makes you jealous;
He's never tired —
You'd think him wired
With electric power —
It makes you sour;
When you're tired out,
And he comes with a shout,
So enthusiastic,
There's something drastic
You'd like to do;
So you throw a shoe,
In one short spasm
Of enthusiasm,
And that's the end,
Of our little friend!

The End
Z is an end,
Zero a beginning;
And so our old world,
Keeps on spinning.